How to
Master
your
Health *and*
Happiness

C000165226

Stephen Ferguson is a master chef, health researcher, athlete, natural bodybuilder, personal trainer and mentor.

He is Britain's Number 1 motivator.

If you would like to contact Stephen Ferguson to speak at your seminar or for another reason, please e-mail Steve.ferguson@live.co.uk.

How to
Master
your
Health *and*
Happiness

Stephen Ferguson

First published in the United Kingdom in 2009
by Mind Books

ISBN 978 0 9562700 0 9

Disclaimer
The views expressed in this book are those of the author, but they are
general views only, and readers are urged to consult a relevant and quali-
fied specialist for individual advice in particular situations. The author
and publisher accept no responsibility for any consequences arising
directly, or indirectly, from advice given herein.

This book is not intended as a substitute for conventional medical advice.
Never stop taking prescribed medicine without first consulting your
doctor. Always inform your doctor of any supplements you are taking, or
plan to take, in case these are contraindicated with your prescribed
medication.

CONTENTS

PREFACE

This is book is going to be one of the most motivating books that you have ever read in your entire life. I can prove from my own knowledge and personal example of achieving a multitude of outstanding goals; that there is nothing that a human being would like to achieve in life that is out of his or her grasp, once they put to work their built-in willpower and self-discipline. All of us have got this, but many of us don't realise it.

Nothing written in this book is mere research only, or things that have happened only in the past. It's how I am and will always continue to be: full of willpower.

In my early 20s I didn't realise I had any willpower at all. I lived a life of eating junk food, drinking beer and going to late-night parties, until one day I said to Mike Williams, a bodybuilding champion in my gym, that I would like to do a bodybuilding competition. He took one look at my 42-inch beer belly, and began to laugh, because he saw how overweight, undisciplined and out of shape I was. But then he said to me;

"Ok … what you have to do is lose weight." He then gave me a diet. I started the diet that very evening, began doing daily exercise and in twelve weeks lost 12 inches off my waist and 5 stones. Three weeks later I came first in the: Mr Titan bodybuilding competition.

On one occasion I was in hospital with a major stomach and bowel disease. The doctors were constantly taking my blood for tests but had no idea what the illness was, and I was just getting weaker and weaker. A friend of a friend died from a similar illness, but I said within myself that this was not going to happen to me. So in my mind I focused on being better. I got up and went downstairs to the hospital canteen, ate a big plate of food, then went back to the ward and within two hours the doctor came and examined me and said I was OK to go home. I had forced myself mentally to complete wellness. The human mind is the most powerful thing on this planet – and that includes *your* mind!

Another example of the fact that everyone has got willpower is the story of Victor Daniels, a performer and writer for the BBC. He got to hear of my capabilities as a motivator, and asked me to be his personal trainer for a month to help him to lose weight.

With the diet that I recommended to him and training him for half an hour, three times a week, he lost 2 stones (approx 14.5kg), in just two weeks!

He struggled to do just eight sit-ups formerly and would never exercise, leading a very comfortable, laid-back life. With just one week of personal training he was doing a straight 150 sit-ups, plus 50 squats and over 100 bicep curls plus much more in just one session.

What helped him to do this? WILLPOWER!

This book will unlock the hidden willpower in you, allowing you to enjoy the happiness that comes from success in achieving your personal goals and taking control of your life. You can eliminate stress and unnecessary problems that come from a lack of willpower and self-discipline, so as to become

A master of your health, fitness and happiness.

1
WHAT *IS*
WILLPOWER?

The man who can drive himself further once the effort gets painful is the man who will win.

Roger Bannister

What is willpower? The dictionary defines it as: a combination of self-discipline and determination to do what is sensible and necessary; the strength of will to carry out one's decisions, wishes or plans; the ability to control one's self and determine one's actions; to exert one's will over one's actions; self-control, decisiveness, resolution and persistence. Or maybe we could simplify it by saying willpower means:

> To have full control of my life and have the capability to do what is necessary to give me happiness and success in the things that I want to achieve in life.

Why is it so vital for us to have willpower in the world that we live in today?

According to a survey, people in Britain spend on average 25 hours a week watching television. Based on current averages, by the age of 80, eleven solid years of your life could have been spent watching Television. Is that the way you want to spend your life? Television is addictive, and despite what you may think, it is not relaxing. It stimulates and tires your brain.

What about advertisements? On average most people are exposed to a minimum of 1,200 adverts every day and of these 76 are mentally noted.

According to the World Health Organization (WHO), 5.4 million people are killed each year from smoking-related diseases. If current trends hold, 1 billion people will die from smoking-related disease this century: 10 times more than in the last one.

Moneyexperts.com, the financial comparisons website, have said of the 13.1 million people in debt, that 40% are worried about their ability to stay on top of those debts.

A survey published in the *Daily Telegraph* states: "The number of overweight people in the world has over-taken the number of malnourished, with over 1 billion people considered heavier than advised. While one in six of the estimated world population of 6.5 billion is now overweight or obese, 800 million do not have enough to eat" (*Daily Telegraph*, 15 August 2006). The article goes on to say that obesity is now affecting developing countries due to dietary changes (including more fatty foods), a decline in physical work, greater car ownership and less active lifestyles. Overweight people run a higher risk of developing diseases such as Type 2 diabetes, heart disease and some cancers.

The World Health Organization describes obesity as "One of the greatest public health challenges of the 21st century". In Britain, as in many European countries, the level of obesity has tripled and is still rising. About two-thirds of British adults are now considered overweight or obese. Of these about a fifth of men and almost a quarter of women are two to three stones overweight. Over the past decade obesity in children has risen markedly, doubling in six-year-olds and trebling among fifteen-year-olds. Obesity and overweight bring with them significant risks of chronic disease and premature death.

In Britain 30% of young women binge drink along with 40% of young men. This usually takes place on Thursday, Friday and Saturday nights for up to seven hours.

According to the British crime survey 2005/2006, it is estimated that 34.9% of 16–59-year-olds have used one or more illicit drugs in their lifetime. 10.5% had used one or more in the last year and 6.3% in the last month.

A survey carried out in the United States by the federal government said that the US has the highest rate of sexually transmitted diseases (STDs) in the industrialised world, with approximately 19 million new infections estimated to occur each year. Women tend to suffer more frequent and more serious complications from STDs than men.

The Office for National Statistics (ONS) stated in a report that if death rates remained unchanged, only 10% of couples marrying in 2008 will make it through to their diamond wedding anniversary. For 45% the marriage will end in divorce and another 45% will end in the death of one of the partners. The chances of relationship breakdown are even greater for cohabiting couples, who have chosen not to marry, but their separations are not a matter of public record and the ONS could not estimate how many of them will stay together for 60 years. It said the number of marriages that would end in divorce increased from 34% among those who tied the knot in 1979 to 41% in 1993 and 45% in 2005. Until the second half of the twentieth century divorce was a relatively rare event. In 1901 there were 512 divorces in England and Wales!

Police figures show that there were 5.6 million crimes in Britain in 2004.

Looking honestly and realistically at all of these statistics what does it help you to see? If a person lacks willpower in the kind of world that we are in today their whole life will be full of unnecessary problems and unhappiness.

We live in a world where 99% of people lack willpower. We could also say, they lack the self-discipline, determination and self-control, to do what's sensible and necessary, to achieve their goals in life that will make them happy. But the thing is: what are those goals, and how can we achieve the goals that we personally want to achieve? This will be discussed in the following chapter.

2

NO *DISCOMFORT,*
NO **PROGRESS**

*The difference between the impossible and possible lies in a
person's determination.*

Tommy Lasorda

Many of the things mentioned in Chapter One give
clear evidence that that we are living in an extremely
undisciplined world where, as I said, 99% of people
lack willpower. So for *you*, the reader of this book, to
develop willpower *you* are going to be going in the
opposite direction to almost everyone else.

So what do you always have to bear in mind?

Developing willpower will make you happy, relieve much
stress, help you to achieve what some think is the impossible – and you will have a better quality of life.

If willpower is such a good thing don't you think that
it is extremely strange that most people haven't got it?
Well you could ask yourself, "why is it that most
people don't own a Rolls Royce?" **There is a price to
pay for everything.**

The statement that I have just made might sound strange, and you might be thinking or saying to yourself, "How on earth can you pay for willpower?"

Now for the moment of truth: the way that you pay for willpower is not with paper money, because if that were the case most people would give almost every penny they have to get it. I'll tell you the currency that willpower is paid for in: it's a four-letter word – **PAIN**.

99% of people today, stay well clear of tapping into that built-in reservoir of willpower, locked deep within them, and all of us, because they can't stand **"DISCOMFORT"**.

You might ask, as many do: "But isn't there an easier way, surely there are many ways to *skin a cat*?" Yes that's true, there are many ways to skin a cat, but there is only one way to unlock willpower, that is locked away within the human machine.

Discomfort means progress: "no discomfort, no progress". I wanted to increase the definition on my lower abdominal muscles. If I spent three minutes training my lower abdominal muscles would that improve them? I could stay in my comfort zone and fantasise to myself, "Oh yes, my lower abdominals are getting much sharper looking." Who though am I fooling? The blunt and bitter truth is that there is no point wasting my money going to the gym if I am going to train like that!

NO DISCOMFORT, NO PROGRESS

That is the complete truth: to progressively unlock willpower within yourself, you must accept within your mind that you *will* experience discomfort. On the other hand, if you try to progressively unlock the willpower within yourself while staying in your comfort zone, you are like me spending three minutes doing inclined sit-ups: something totally unthinkable! Putting it plainly you are wasting your time. Your willpower stays locked away when you stay in your comfort zone. The key to opening the door to willpower within you is discomfort and pain. From this point onwards, kiss your comfort zone goodbye. If you don't, throw this book in the bin. You are wasting your time reading it.

Previously I said that I wanted to improve my lower abdominal muscles, and, this was true. So what I did was three sets of 20 repetitions, which for me, if I am honest with myself, is keeping me in my comfort zone. If I rarely did sit-ups or if I had just started going to the gymnasium, that amount of sit-ups would be sufficient to cause me enough discomfort to improve my lower abdominal muscles – but I have been going to the gym regularly for 23 years! The way I was able to improve my lower abdominal muscles, was when I took part in a bodybuilding competition and saw someone at that competition who had excellent abdominal muscles. I said to him, "What did you do to get such excellent abs?" He replied, "Three sets of 100 inclined sit-ups." So I went away and thought about what he said and the next training session that I did in the gymnasium, I did 50 repetitions, and I must admit, this did, bring me out of my comfort zone. I felt much discomfort and I progressed a little bit. But for the goal that I set for myself, and the high standard that I wanted to achieve, I needed to go further out of my comfort zone and deeper into the zone of discomfort. So the next training session, I did one set of 200 repetitions then another set of 100 repetitions; There was major improvement in my lower abdominal muscles. But again, the standard I wanted to achieve was still higher. The next time that I visited the gymnasium I pushed myself to do a straight 320 repetitions on the inclined sit-ups bench, followed by other exercises for my abdominal muscles. Now I have reached my goal! I have the joy of an excellent set of abdominal muscles (a "six-pack"). I applied the same method to getting my legs, and all of my other body parts in the perfect shape for me. I pushed myself out of my comfort zone, into a zone of discomfort, so that I could progress to have my body in the exact perfect shape that I wanted. No discomfort, no improvement.

This might sound so vain and selfish. But, it's not. There is no greater motivator than *example*. When people see how your willpower has increased and anything that you choose to do in life, you are able to do, any goals that you set for yourself you are able to attain – that in itself will be a great inspiration to them!

Why is a plane able to take off with the wind against it? While in flight why is it able to withstand air pressure, turbulence and all of the other outside elements lashing against it?

Much time and effort has been invested into making that plane as strongly built as possible; so that come what may, the plane can hold itself together, and all of the passengers on board the plane, can reach their destination safely. That analogy is to illustrate what willpower will do for you: it takes time and effort, but it will make you as strongly built as possible, so that whatever turbulence or pressures might come your way, you will be able to hold yourself together, to finally reach your destination safely, which is, to achieve your goals.

How much do you desire your goals?

That is a soul-searching question that you need to ask yourself. No one in their right mind is going to pay £50,000 for a Rolls Royce that hasn't got an engine in it. The same is true with regards to your goals also: if you think that pain and discomfort are too high a price to pay for your goals, either change your goals or force yourself to love and appreciate the goals that you already have.

You might ask; "how I can force myself to love and appreciate the goals that I already have, when I don't love them enough to go through pain and discomfort to achieve them?"

Become a deep thinker

Some of the greatest people, with the most willpower, that ever walked this earth, were deep thinkers.

What you need to do is think deeply about your goals and do a bit of soul-searching. Ask yourself: "Why do I want to achieve this goal? What's in it for me? How will I feel when I have achieved this goal?"

What you can do also is picture yourself having actually achieved the goal that you want to achieve. Many world class athletes picture in their minds crossing the finishing line first and how they would feel wearing the gold medal. These thoughts drive them to be a winner, and achieve awards in their particular sport.

I used that concept when I was washing dishes in a small Italian restaurant. The head chef told me that I was useless and another chef told me that the head chef was planning to sack me and to round it all off, he was paying me one-fifth of the wages that the other two kitchen porters were getting. I left that job and got sacked from another job. Another restaurant told me that my cooking skills were so bad that I should change my profession. But in my mind I had always pictured working in a top Michelin-starred restaurant with some of the best chefs in the world, and eventually I did achieve my goal. Not only did I get to be one of the number one chefs in that restaurant, but I worked in a number of five-star hotel kitchens with some outstanding chefs and today I am a master chef knowing how to cook almost every dish there is.

> Any goal you want can be achieved with willpower. Picture yourself there.

As I said in my last analogy, someone who has got willpower never gives up. I know for me giving up is not in my vocabulary and I will never let it in. When you try something one way, if it doesn't work, try another way – regardless of how many times you have to try. **Never give up!**

Take for instance the example of Abraham Lincoln. **Abraham didn't give up:**

1831	Failed in business – declared bankruptcy.
1832	Ran for State Legislature – lost.
1834	Failed in business – declared bankruptcy.
1835	Wife-to-be died.
1836	Had a nervous breakdown.
1837	Election – lost.
1843	Ran for US Congress – lost.
1846	Ran for US Congress – lost
1847	Ran for US Congress – lost.
1855	Ran for US Senate – lost.
1856	Ran for office of Vice President – lost.
1858	Ran for US Senate – lost.
1859	Elected President of the USA – Won! Wow!

Don't you think Abraham Lincoln is an outstanding example of someone who refused give up, come what may? Many in the history books have had a similar attitude.

What about *you*, the reader: is your mind set ready to blast forward with that level of willpower?

You might say to yourself; "I could never be like that in a million years!" But as I said earlier in this book, all of us have willpower locked deep within us.

Acceptance

Abraham Lincoln accepted that progress wasn't going to be easy. He knew that pain and discomfort are necessities. No discomfort, no progress: he didn't fantasise about success when he hadn't reached it. Success was a burning desire within his soul and nothing could stop him from coming back to claim victory.

The turbulence that was clearly evident in his life only made him stronger and more determined, creating within him a super-human iron will.

Whatever goals *you* have, attack them with the same force and vigour. Refuse to give up.

In this chapter we have seen that 99% of people on this earth lack willpower and more than likely will never have it. But on the other hand people would love to have the benefits that come from having willpower and self-discipline; but they are not prepared to pay the price. Most people want effortless progress, which, unfortunately does not exist (it's a fairy story).

No discomfort, no growth; the more discomfort the more growth. If I want my bicep muscles to grow half an inch, the more painful and vigorous I make my workouts, the quicker I will stimulate growth in my bicep muscles, so that they can grow half an inch. It's the same with willpower: the more inner strength that you are willing to use and the effort to push past and fight against feelings of laziness, the more of an iron will you develop and the more you can take full control of your life.

Earlier in this chapter you were encouraged to kiss your comfort zone goodbye, and the mere fact that you are still reading this book through to this point means that you have done so, otherwise this book would now be in the bin.

I also stated the fact that increasing your will power so that you can achieve the goals that you really want is not selfish; example is the best motivator.

When people see how powerful and strong your willpower is and how you make life look so easy, also all of the outstanding goals that you have set for yourself and achieved, that will motivate them to want to do the same.

In some ways, you will be doing something to help society, and what can be nobler than that?

You must create within yourself a burning passion, a fire, a love and appreciation for your goal and if this doesn't happen naturally you will have to do it manually by becoming a deep thinker.

Think deeply about your goal and why it is so vitally important that you achieve it. Don't let anything get in your way, never ever give up.

In the next chapter we are going to look at some specific goals that you might have.

3
ACHIEVE *YOUR*
GOALS

Nothing great will ever be achieved without great men, and men are great only if they are determined to be so.

Charles De Gaulle

What are your goals? Here are some examples. I'm not saying that these should be your goals. You can personally have any goals that you want, that will improve your life and make you happy.

Stop smoking	Swim the channel
Watch less TV	Get a better job
Lose weight	Earn more money
Spend less	Win a sports competition
Save money	Drink less alcohol
Start exercising	Pass an exam
Eat healthily	Become physically stronger
Eat less	Become mentally stronger
Run a marathon	

All of these goals and more are possible once we open up that willpower within us and also realise no discomfort, no progress.

Improve health

Let's take the first one: suppose your goal was to give up smoking, lose weight or do something else to improve your health. As we said in Chapter 1, 5.4 billion people are killed each year from smoking-related diseases and one-sixth of the 6.5 billion people on earth are now obese. So for you to have goals like these would be excellent.

But the problem with most people is that when it comes to having goals like this, instead of them thinking to themselves, "I would be so much healthier if I were to give up smoking, lose weight or improve my health in some other way", they wait for the doctor to say, "Unless you stop smoking, lose weight or improve your health in some other way, your life expectancy will be only another 5 years." Then they work hard to improve their health.

Those of us with strong willpower do not wait for doctors and medical specialists to choose for us what we should be doing in life, or what is the most sensible course of action to proceed with: we choose for ourselves. Strong willpower has given us that freedom to do what we should be doing, when we should be doing it.

Set a definite date to start to improve your health. Don't let someone else decide when *you* – the one having an iron will – will stop smoking, lose weight or improve your health in another way (for example cut down on your junk food consumption or the quantity of alcohol that you drink).

Have your own personal reason for stopping a bad habit.

Bad habits, including smoking, over-eating or heavy drinking, are usually part of a routine of events. What you will need to do is change your daily routine to a more positive one, that will have a positive effect on your overall wellbeing.

When I first began losing weight, I used to cycle to work every day and because I was getting fitter, I felt better within myself; I could see the positive benefits that came from working on losing weight, and that motivated me to continue.

Just think how much fitter you will feel when you stop allowing the 4,000 chemicals that are contained in cigarettes to go into your heart, lungs and bloodstream. Also when you stop allowing all of the free radicals into your body that can eventually give you cancer.

Even during the first twenty-four hours when you stop smoking, most of the carbon monoxide will come out of your blood stream. After one year, the risk of suffering a heart attack, is reduced by half. After ten years of stopping, your risk of developing lung cancer is reduced by half and after fifteen years your risk of heart attack falls to that of a non smoker.

Try to always have a positive point of view. All athletes – even Olympic ones – have the odd bad day maybe because of injury, sickness or some other reason, so if you have an odd day when you have a smoking blip or a blip in sticking to your diet or the diets contained in this book, don't give up.

The benefits that come from eliminating smoking and eating in an unhealthy way from your life, forever, far outweigh the temporary enjoyment from smoking, eating junk food and not exercising.

If you were walking up the stairs and you tripped on a step would you go all of the way to the bottom of the stairs and start again, or say "I'm going to the bottom of those stairs and I'm never going to climb stairs ever again!" Of course you wouldn't! So do the same with your smoking, junk food or lack of exercise habit, never allow anything to knock you off-course from your goal.

While I was progressing toward getting my body into a healthy ripped state, I would picture how it would feel when my body was exactly how I wanted it, and this helped to increase my willpower. Or we could say, to break things down a bit further, this helped to increase my discipline, determination and mental strength of will to achieve my goal.

Use the discomfort that comes from working continually toward kicking your bad habits to make you mentally stronger. No discomfort, no progress. The human body craves comfort: when we go outside our comfort zone into a zone of discomfort, the imperfect subconscious mind will do everything in its power to push us back to the comfort zone.

As was said in Chapter One, 99% of people on this earth today, go through the whole of their lives in a comfort zone, almost helpless to the desires and pressures put before them in this world. Not only that, but they are also helpless to emotional desires and struggles within themselves, which in turn causes them to be weak-minded and unhappy within themselves because of having no control. To take it further, they have low self-esteem and lack confidence, and are unable to force themselves to do what they want, or we could say, will.

Before you even try to stop smoking, eat healthily or exercise regularly, you should have a master plan. If you remember, in Chapter Two of this book we considered becoming a deep thinker. Think about the reality of what is necessary for you to stop smoking, eat healthily or exercise regularly, or in other words, accept the reality of what is involved, also the reality of what smoking and an unhealthy lifestyle is actually doing to your body.

Try to think back to when you have tried to stop smoking, or start dieting and exercising in the past, that is if you have tried to do this in the past, and remember what happened. You were constantly craving for a cigarette or craving for food, or if we are looking at reducing your alcohol consumption, you were constantly craving alcohol. Maybe if you have tried to do a regular exercise routine in the past, after three weeks or so you gave up.

Think also of the excuses that your subconscious mind made:

"Oh, smoking eases my stress."

"Smoking relaxes me."

"Some people smoke until the age of 90 and they're OK."

Or in the case of a food diet:

"This diet is giving me a headache."

"I feel weak and dizzy."

"It's too painful and it will make me ill."

"Our bodies need a large quantity of food."

"One chocolate or cake isn't going to hurt". Then one turns into two or three every day.

Or with regards to alcohol consumption:

"Come on just one last drink, it's not going to hurt."

As was mentioned earlier in this book most people on this earth are controlled by their sub-conscious mind because they live in a comfort zone.

I said in the Preface of this book, that before I had the desire to do a bodybuilding competition, I had a 42-inch stomach. I wasn't a heavy smoker but I would smoke in company, I wouldn't go a day without alcohol and junk food, and I would spend most of my time in front of the TV or sleeping. I suffered from asthma since childhood and the lifestyle that I led previously aggravated my illness. I was spending hundreds of pounds each year on inhalers and used them throughout the day. I was also regularly in and out of hospital. My doctor said that I visited his surgery more than any other patient he had and it was getting to the point whereby he was starting to get sick of seeing me!

The thing that really moved and motivated me to change from being an undisciplined couch potato to the extremely self-disciplined person that I am today was my desire to want the best for myself. I wanted my health to be the best it could possibly be and I also wanted to achieve all of my personal goals and my life to be as happy as possible.

That's the attitude that *you*, the reader of this book, have now got, bearing in mind that you're at this stage of the book. Let that attitude drive you forward to stop living in an unhealthy way forever. After changing my lifestyle, I hardly ever used inhalers for my asthma, I am extremely fit, and my body is in very good condition, (ripped). I want the standard, or if you would like to call it the quality, of my life to still get higher, so I still keep pushing myself further into a zone of discomfort.

When dieting I try to keep in my house only the type of food that is beneficial for my diet. I either throw in the bin or refrain from buying the type of food that is detrimental to my diet. Do the same with your smoking habit or unhealthy eating. Get rid of everything in your house that is associated with smoking: ashtrays, cigarettes, the lot! Change your whole smoking routine. Or when it comes to losing weight, get rid of any food that will cause you to put on weight.

When you are focusing on losing weight, don't worry about saying to yourself, "There are people starving around the world, so I mustn't throw this food away."

That is a true and very good moral statement, but when you are in the process of losing weight you must not focus on that thought, you have to focus on losing weight, which means eating less, eating healthily and exercising regularly. So as I have just said: throw out what won't help your diet.

If you cook too much food, either give it away or throw it away. This is your new life. If something triggers a relapse into smoking or unhealthy eating or living habits, analyse what caused it and eliminate that thing out of your life.

Isn't it so amazing that giving up any bad habit basically takes the same process?

What I have written throughout this book definitely works because I have done it. I am a living example.

A strong-willed, strong-minded person never gives up. When they fall they just refocus, and re-analyse, and then push forward once again, accepting that this road that is being walked is an uncomfortable one.

Get aggressive with yourself. When an athlete wants to achieve something beyond his natural every-day ability, to get adrenaline flowing in his body, he works himself up, gets angry with himself.

When I feel a bit burnt-out in the gymnasuim, that's

what I do to myself. It helps to get my willpower working and adrenaline rushing through my veins.

Do whatever it takes to kick your smoking habit, your unhealthy diet or lack of regular physical exercise out of this universe!

Most bodybuilders, myself included, will tell you that they train better in the environment of a gymnasium where there are other people, rather than at home on their own. Being surrounded by others who care about their bodies, and in most cases love their bodies, is a strong motivation to give a person. So why not do the same, by telling your family members and friends about your goal to give up smoking, start dieting or regularly exercising; this will be a strong motivation for you to increase your ability to go through the discomfort of stopping smoking, sticking to your diet and starting a regular exercise routine.

If you recall, in Chapter two of this book, it stated that to go through the pain and discomfort involved with developing willpower, you must have a good reason, a passion for going through it.

It was also stated that no one is going to pay £50,000 for a Rolls Royce that has not got an engine!

To build that passion in you, write down a list of reasons why you want to stop smoking, start eating healthily, start eating less and exercising regularly. Carry it around with you, memorise it, until you have a burning desire to stop smoking, start dieting and start exercising regularly.

Your mind controls everything about you

If you think and focus your mind on happy positive things, that will become your natural way of thinking. It's much easier to achieve your goals when you think in a happy positive way.

Regularly repeat to yourself, "I control my thoughts, they don't control me", and actually put this into action and this will be a strong motivation toward more willpower, achieving your goals and greater happiness.

So we are now getting to the end of our discussion on smoking, healthy eating and regular exercise. How are you going to feel while you are trying to stop smoking, start dieting or exercising regularly?

You will feel similar to a drug addict trying to come off cocaine or some other hard drug, because remember nicotine is a drug contained in cigarettes and is very addictive. So you will have anxiety attacks, headaches, irritability, cravings and it's also normal for a smoker's cough to worsen as the airways come back to life. Reward yourself when you go a long time without a cigarette.

It's interesting that you will get similar symptoms when you start to diet because your body hates to change and is built to protect itself and give you warnings when it feels endangered. You will feel weak, get headaches, be irritabile and start to really crave the food that you have stopped eating or cut down on. These symptoms are all normal – just keep going.

If symptoms get to an extreme level only in the case of a food diet, increase your intake of food just for that day, then start the diet again the next day.

Always drink plenty of water.

But remember that the goal is not to go long periods of time without a cigarette or overindulging in alcoholic beverage, but to destroy, get rid of the habit forever.

The same thing applies to eating in a healthy way or doing regular physical exercise, it's something that's not just for a limited period of time, but is now your new lifestyle!

Control other habits

To watch less television requires the same mental attitude and that's one of resistance. You have to occupy your mind with more productive things, things that are important to you, then mentally force yourself to stop these habits, while focusing on how beneficial and productive the sensible use of your time is and how strong-willed you are becoming.

Remember your happiness will come from being successful in the things that you desire and love. As always, of course, there is going to be initial discomfort, but I'm sure you expect that.

Nothing of lasting good comes without a little bit of pain, to say the least.

Good budgeting

To budget wisely, you need to write down all of your monthly, or weekly expense, and then, add them all together. After that, subtract your expenses, from the amount that you earn, and this will leave you with the amount that you are able to save each month. Once you have established the amount of money that you can save each month, here is where you have to use your mental strength and willpower to force yourself away from the things that you are usually tempted to buy and instead save the money. You will get many emotional desires to spend, spend, spend, but you must ignore them if you are to make progress with regards to budgeting wisely.

In this chapter we have looked at having the willpower needed to conquer smoking, the health benefits that come from a person that stops smoking and the reality of the struggle, pain and discomfort that a person will face, when they try to stop.

We also looked at the importance of having a healthy diet and regular exercise. We saw too, that the same mental attitude and technique needed for giving up smoking can also be applied when a person wants to diet so as to lose weight, or do some form of regular exercise.

In the next chapter we are going to look at how good time management can help you to achieve so many goals, or we could say give you the time to achieve so many goals, in your life.

4

TIME
MANAGEMENT

*Without goals, and plans to reach them, you are like a ship that
has set sail with no destination.*

Fitzhugh Dodson

Only 24 hours per day

In this chapter we are going to look at the fact that there
are only 24 hours in a day, and most of us have to work
at least 8 hours a day, if not more. We also need to sleep
6–8 hours per night for good health, and, eat and drink.
All of this takes time, but it doesn't end there. Cooking
a meal may take anything from 45 minutes to an hour.
Don't forget getting ready for work and travelling to
work: all of that could take 3 hours. If you have children you would have to get your children ready also,
and give them their breakfast. When your children
return from school, they will want you to play with
them, or help them to do their homework.

Once all of this is finished, you are only left with
about 3–4 hours each weekday. So that begs the ques-

tion, what are you going to do, with that small fraction of time, that you have left? Bearing in mind that you have got to this point in the book, I'm sure that you are going to spend your time, focusing on your goals. I will tell you what 99% of people do with their 3–4 hours: they spend it in front of the television set, watching their favourite programmes, or DVDs, or just relaxing to some music, or doing some other form of recreation.

So to put it plainly, 99% of people, love to spend their 3–4 hours of time in their comfort zone. If they had more time, they would spend *even longer* in their comfort zone. As I have just written I'm sure you're not someone like that who just wants to waste their life away.

Give me more time

One place that you can get more time from, is to watch less television, or better still no television. By now, I am sure that you have got the willpower, to stop yourself from doing anything! The way that you can watch less television, is to circle the programmes that you want to watch, and only watch those ones. **No channel flicking!**

Why would this be so beneficial to you?

As was mentioned in Chapter One, people in Britain spend a vast amount of time watching television it is addictive. Television causes your mind to switch off. For those of us who are trying to rapidly increase our willpower, it's destroying our chances of that, because strong willpower comes from a strong mind. By resisting the desire to spend, or we could say waste, most of your time watching television you will be able to think freely for yourself, without having someone's make-believe life control your thoughts and make your mind weak.

For my body to stay in good shape and be very strong, I have to eat healthily, and make sure, that, good carbohydrates, proteins and vitamins are contained, in the food, that I allow to go into my body. I have to make sure also, that I experience discomfort when I am training my body in the gymnasium, otherwise, my body will start to become weaker. The mind is exactly the same: if you allow weak, make-believe things to enter your mind, it makes it weaker. But on the other hand if you keep feeding your mind, strong realistic things, that will motivate willpower.

The Bible says: "He that is walking with wise persons, will become wise (Proverbs 13:20)." Another famous saying is, "Show me your friends and I will show you who you are." Whether it is strong-minded, motivated friends, or programmes on television, that motivate you, those are the thoughts you want to feed your mind with.

Instead of music that only relaxes you most of the time, try listening to music that motives and stimulates you mentally. That will be wise use of your time, and be an aid to developing strong willpower. I am sure that you have heard the saying: "You are what you eat". Your mind and thinking are the same, and even more so, because your mind controls your whole body, your feelings, your goals, your desires – everything about *you*. So you need to be very careful to look after your mind, more than any other body part that you have, and put strong things into it, doing so, will motivate you to have strong willpower and a strong disciplined mind.

The survey referred to earlier in this book mentioned "because television is so addictive, when a person tries to stop they find themselves doing it again". If you find that you have got that problem, then what you have to do is throw the television away or put it into the attic, or a cupboard, out of the way and fill your time doing other things.

Have a written schedule

The quotation at the beginning of this chapter describes the behaviour of human beings very well. Unless we have a set of definite goals to achieve, we are like; "a ship that has set sail with no destination".

What can help you to overcome, this natural tendency that we humans have in us? Have a written schedule. Before you start each day, have a "to do" list. Write down where you need to be, what you need to do and when you need to do it. Now you are really starting to get your willpower working.

If you think back to what was written in Chapter

One, willpower: "is the ability to control one's self and determine one's actions; to exert one's will over one's actions; self-control, decisiveness, resolution and persistence". Or maybe we could simplify it by saying willpower means **to have full control of my life and have the capability to do what is necessary to give me happiness and success in the things that I want to achieve in life.**

Your schedule, will allow you to have full control over your life and your time. Because this may be a new concept to you, you will experience negative thoughts telling you that writing everything down is a waste of precious time: "I can just remember the things that I have to do in my head" you may say. What you have to do then is try one day whereby you write everything down and then the next day don't write everything down, and see which day is more productive for you. It's obvious which will be more productive, but it's just to convince your mind, so that you can make it your new good habit.

Start your schedule now

This schedule will cause you to advance a great deal in your time management, but I have to remind you of this once again: where there is advancement there is pain and discomfort. A schedule is a weapon that is taking you out of a zone of comfort into a zone of discomfort and productivity. This leads to progress in the things that you want to achieve and finally happiness. Now that you have read this, why not start now? The longer you leave it, the harder it will be to get going when you do want to start.

Another useful habit that you can cultivate is to prepare meals in advance. During the weekend try cooking a variety of different nutritious healthy meals. You can separate the meals into 5 or 6 plastic containers and put them in the freezer. Defrost a tub each day to feed yourself and your family.

Once again this will require you to leave a zone of comfort. When busy you may cheat yourself and settle for a takeaway, or just settle for losing that precious time. You now have to discipline and organise yourself so that your meals are arranged appropriately.

I personally like to cook my food a week in advance and I go shopping just once a week. In this way, I have got as much time as possible to focus on my goals.

What about you? What are you going to do with all of this free time that you now have?

You can use your free time to start working for yourself rather than being employed by someone, and work the hours each day that you desire to work, rather than someone else dictating them to you.

You can do some volunteer work, maybe in the kind of work that you have always desired to do, but never had the time.

Many people enjoy volunteer work, because it is usually for a cause that is valuable in their eyes, so it brings a sense of deep satisfaction.

Remember, the whole purpose of developing willpower, is to increase your happiness and health, and have the absolute best for yourself.

If you're a religiously inclined person, you might want to set spiritual goals for yourself.

An excellent goal that you can set for yourself, is to join a gym. I am sure you know the saying "healthy body, healthy mind". Bearing in mind we are trying to increase our willpower, so whatever activities we can get involved in, that encourage increased development of willpower or mental strength, we surely want to be involved in them.

The need for speed

When I worked in a certain five-star hotel, we would have what was called a '*mis en place*' list. This was a list of things which had to be prepared that morning before the customers arrived to dine, or in simple terms preparation prior to service. At times there could be about forty items or more on your preparation list, so the motto in the kitchen was **"Always have a sense of urgency"**. Everything needed to be completed in a rush, while still keeping up the high standards. You can apply something similar in your life: give yourself deadlines on your "to do" list. Write exactly what time you would like each task on your list to be completed, you will then see how much extra time that will give you.

One thing that you have to understand about time is that it will never just appear, you have to put in the effort, yes, use your willpower to gain that time. I would like to remind you again, there is only one way to *skin a cat* in this game and that's by leaving your comfort zone and moving into a zone of discomfort – then you will progress toward having much more time.

A rich man once asked his gardener to plant a tree. The gardener rejected the idea, saying that the tree would take too long to grow, and not reach maturity for 100 years. The rich man replied to the gardener, "In that case there is no time to lose. Plant it this afternoon!" You can do a similar thing so that your strength of will keeps growing: act now!

Never procrastinate

As you know, no one is perfect, our minds can play tricks on us. If we procrastinate, or make excuses with regards to why we shouldn't do a certain thing or why it can be left till tomorrow, we are weakening our strength of will and start to decline into a state of becoming weak-willed again. If a bodybuilder who formerly did intense workouts, with reasonably heavy weights, suddenly changed to working with light weights during a less intense workout, his muscles will immediately start to become weaker. If this bodybuilder wants improvement and progress, he will need to increase the weight that he is using, which would then remove him from his comfort zone into a zone of discomfort. Once he does this progress and growth will occur.

Effortless and painless progress is what most people want and even crave. There is no such thing, and it's just a dream and fantasy.

Every second is precious

Most of the time today, when you make a telephone call to a company, you are likely to be left waiting on the line. Rather than getting frustrated because you are kept on the line for so long, use your newly found willpower to utilise the time wisely:

- Read a book
- Do work on your laptop
- Organise your schedule

Do whatever productive thing you would like to with your newly found time. The same principle can be applied when:

- Travelling on the tube
- Travelling on the bus
- Sitting in the doctor's waiting room
- Waiting for the tube
- Waiting for the bus

- Sitting in the hairdresser's
- Sitting in the barber's

And any other area that you can think of where time gets wasted. I have observed, what most people do when they are waiting at a bus stop or doctor's surgery. They sit staring at one another, and obviously wasting time.

I always try to carry a bag with me, that has a pen and a pad in it, just in case I get ideas to put in my book that I am writing at the time. I also carry books and audio recordings so that while I am travelling or waiting about anywhere my productivity never stops. I never want to stop my willpower from growing stronger.

Constantly keep analysing your time, always try to squeeze things into your life that will help you to move closer to achieve your life goals.

The extra time that you now have can be used to study for an exam, or you might be someone doing a course of some sort – that time may also be used to prepare coursework.

No excuses

The large majority of people that take up some form of physical exercise, quit before the third week of training.

What are some common excuses that most humans make?

Problem	Excuse
Lack of willpower	I am not strong enough
No exercise	I will start – never happens
Good diet	I can't, it's too hard
Overweight	I start well, but can't keep going
Smoking	It helps with stress
Under stress	There's just so much to do
Debt	I can't help spending
Procrastination	I need a rest

The fact that you can now manage your time wisely, and you understand how to get your willpower working properly, means that none of these excuses will stand in your way, to stop you achieve your goals.

In this chapter we have seen that after all of the normal daily activities have taken place there are only 3–4 hours left in the day to achieve our goals.

We have also seen that 99% of people waste their 3–4 hours daily, watching television: not that there is anything wrong with watching televison, but we need to try to watch things that will be beneficial to us mentally and not drain us mentally. We have also learnt that television is addictive; we think it relaxes but it actually agitates and tires the mind.

We need to use time wisely when waiting in a doctor's surgery, on a plane, a bus, a train, or at any other time that we find ourselves sitting about waiting. We can read a book, plan our schedule, or perhaps do work on a laptop. Don't procrastinate or make excuses. Applying the things written in this chapter, will help to relieve much of your daily stress, and remember – certain kinds of stress damage your health. Applying the things contained in this chapter will also aid you, by improving the way in which you manage your time. It will increase your strength of will which will be beneficial to your whole life and make you happier.

All humans have similar needs. I'm sure you've heard the saying "early to bed, early to rise, keeps you healthy, wealthy, and wise". It's an obvious fact that unless a person looks after their health their life will be a misery. It's certainly not a nice feeling to be on numerous medication for most of your life. During my younger days I experienced what it was like to be constantly on medication. The side-effects of medication are basically slowly killing you. So, in the next chapter we are going to look at keeping good health. I would like to remind you of this; unless someone possesses strong willpower, which is: "a combination of self-discipline and determination, or we could say the mental strength of will, to overcome their natural emotional desires to force themselves to do what is beneficial to them", they will never attain good health. "No discomfort, no progress". If you want comfort, the end results are a lot more painful than becoming a person with strong willpower.

5

GOOD *HEALTH* – THE *IMPORTANCE* OF **W**ATER

Ill-health of body or mind is defeat. Health alone is victory. Let all men, if they can manage it, contrive to be healthy!

Thomas Carlyle

In Chapter One we considered the facts on obesity and binge drinking. Based on those facts, it is clear that the majority of people do not take care of their health that well, either because they are not bothered, too busy or they are ignorant about doing so. This all boils down to a lack of willpower, which includes self-discipline. A self-disciplined person has got order and control in their life.

Good health

To gain a high standard of health, a person needs to care for their physical wellbeing, and look after their emotional wellbeing. The thing that usually causes us the most stress, is not having control over our lives – *life* controls us instead of *us* controlling life.

Let's take a look at our emotional wellbeing first of all. To have good emotional stability in our lives, we need to have peace in our lives. So you need to take a good look at your life, and see if there are any areas that are robbing you of peace and where adjustments need to be made. A self-disciplined person leads a peaceful, orderly life.

We need to treat people well, and that starts with the people in our own house, whether that is a flat-mate or family members. It is not only family members who need to be treated well: we should treat everyone we come into contact with well. This will have a beneficial effect on them, and it will be a natural reaction in most cases for people to do the same back to us. If you think well of people you will treat them well and will get the same back. We all know the cliché "What goes around comes back around", and "You reap what you sow". So what we can see from this is, that if you treat others well you will be treated well by them and this will bring peace into your life.

Another way of bringing peace into your life, so as to benefit your emotional health, is similar to a point written in Chapter Four: we need to be careful of what we allow into our minds. An example of the effect that what we watch has on us is; when we watch something on television or at the cinema that is quite sad.

How does that make us feel? In many cases the story, although it's make-believe, may still bring a tear or two to most people's eyes.

Our brain, finds it extremely difficult to distinguish between what is make-believe from what is real. I'm sure you have heard the phrase "You are what you eat". This holds true also with our mind; we are what we allow our minds to feed on.

It's not my place to tell you how to entertain yourself, but the best things to fill your mind with are what will cause you to grow in intelligence and sensibleness. Our brain has neurons in it, these neurons respond to stimuli and communicate the presence of stimuli to the central nervous system. The central nervous system processes that information, and sends responses to other parts of the body for action. Put simply, whatever information we allow to keep passing through the neurons in our brain, builds grooves, and that information becomes our personality or disposition.

If we were to have no respect for our body, and live on junk food, our health and body would be like junk, overweight, and we would be killing ourselves. The same is true with our minds: fill your mind with junk and it robs you of peace, because your decisions will be reflected in the way you think and you will be basically destroying your mind. "Good food, good body, good mental food, good mind" and a peaceful life: this will give you good emotional health.

The following will also keep you emotionally healthy:

- A tidy, clean house in good repair
- A tidy desk
- A clean body (wash and clean your teeth twice a day)
- Your clothes ironed and put away
- Washing done
- Washing up done and put away
- Dress in a clean, tidy and professional manner
- Cook healthy, nutritious meals each day
- Write a schedule each day to organise your life and time
- Keep your email account organised and tidy
- Budget wisely – save money

A self-disciplined person has their life in order, this helps to keep them emotionally healthy. A good exercise you can do, is, look at the list above and try to see if there are any areas in your life where you need to improve. Use your newly found willpower to adjust these areas.

Our brain works in a way whereby it naturally likes order, and works at its best when things are in order. If you looked at an advert for a holiday home, or hotel room, and the beds were not made, and the rooms were dirty and disorganised, would you be motivated to stay there if you were planning to go on holiday? Of course not! We need to have our life in order, to be mentally and emotionally healthy.

Physical health

The first thing you need to do when you want to look after your physical health is to be brutally honest with yourself, about your current state of health. Say to yourself, "This is where I am, and this is where I am going." In the Preface I made the point that; in my early 20s I didn't realise I had any willpower at all.

Before I started my diet, I had to accept the fact that my stomach or waist *was* 42 inches. I also had to accept realistically how uncomfortable it was going to be for me to get my body into shape. I had to recognise there was no other way to improve my health than to come out of my comfort zone into a zone of discomfort, for me to move forward with better health. I put pictures on my bedroom wall of the type of body I wanted and would regularly imagine myself like that. I went a step further and imagined how it would feel being like that. This increased my desire for that kind of body, and I finally achieved it.

Water is vital for health

Why is water so important for our health? Water is used for almost everything in your body, it's a bit like the conveyer belt that transports nutrients to your organs. For many years, in my ignorance, my "water" was Tenants Super (strong beer – 9% alcohol) and at times a bottle of white wine to wash it down. I wasn't an alcoholic whereby I would get completely drunk and *off my head*, but what I would do is use alcohol to relieve stress. This behaviour caused me to have quite high blood pressure and I would regularly suffer from nose bleeds.

The truth is, when our bodies come under different stresses, an increased water intake is the thing that helps us to cope with these stresses.

Water is vital for our brains to work properly. The human brain is 1.36kg for men and 1.25kg in weight for women, so it's not extremely heavy, but 1 litre of blood passes through our brains every minute. Isn't that absolutely amazing! The brain's tissue is 80% water.

When you get a headache, you probably think nothing of it, and take a couple of painkillers then forget about it, if it's not too bad. I would regularly get headaches and carry painkillers everywhere with me. Since I increased my water intake and cleaned up my diet, I very rarely get headaches. In fact I can't remember the last time that I had one.

If the body doesn't get enough water it lets us know by its built-in alarm signals. One of the simple ones, is in the form of a headache. It's a bit like a machine that is not regularly oiled; eventually it will seize up and not work properly. I was like most people today, who drink nowhere near enough water. If they get thirsty instead of wisely drinking water, they drink tea, coffee and sugary drinks. Although it is true that these drinks do contain water, the problem with them is they contain ingredients that cause the human body to become dehydrated. When this form of lifestyle is continued it eventually leads to the breakdown of the body's organs, chronic illness and eventual death. I must admit I did continue this lifestyle for quite some time and I began to suffer from gastroenteritis – and had to take numerous types of medication for this, that had other side effects, causing me to take other medication for other illnesses. Yes, as you can tell, it's a never-ending cycle.

Please do yourself a big favour like I have done to myself: **Drink more and more water!**

When you get dehydrated, your body will give you a signal to alert you to the fact that you are dehydrated (similar to an athlete, when running, may feel a twitch in his hamstring, but if he continues to run, his hamstring tears). When our bodies become dehydrated we feel pain.

The natural inclination of people who experience pain is to go to the doctor, and the doctor will in most cases prescribe some sort of drug for the patient. What these drugs are actually doing is masking a real need for increased regular water intake. It's like your car needing oil to lubricate the different parts of its engine. Instead of putting oil into the engine of the car, you put margarine, which will lubricate the engine, but the engine will still seize up eventually. If water deficiency continues, the sickness will continue and in some cases it may lead to death by dehydration.

Realising how an increased regular water intake can prevent sickness and also in most cases cure sickness will certainly save you money, if you pay for your health care. Because water is so readily available many people take it for granted, and don't really appreciate its curing and prevention of sickness values.

An example of the power that water has for keeping good health is myself. I have suffered with asthma all of my life. I wrote earlier in this book, formerly I would use my inhaler every day, but since I increased my water intake along with a healthy diet and exercise, I almost never have to use it. The drugs that we are given by doctors usually never cure things like high blood pressure, asthma, ulcers, and arthritis. It has been possible in some cases to cure (and possibly prevent) these illnesses by an increased water intake.

When we get a dry mouth, we may think that this is a sign that tells us that we need to drink water, but the real truth is that this is the last outward sign of the need of water. Once this situation continues we start to damage our bodies. Going back to the analogy of the car, if the owner of the car recognises that his car needs oil early enough, he can prevent much damage to his car. Similarly, recognising how vital an increased water intake is can prevent much damage to our bodies.

Water is the thing that transports all of the nutrients around our bodies to the different organs. All of our organs' functions are monitored by water. The disease that a person will get depends a lot on the organ that is short of water.

I am sure these truths so far about the importance of increasing your water intake, have motivated you to drink more water. You will be happier and healthier.

Old age

Another analogy to show the importance of drinking water is the fact that a plant may get nutrients from the soil, and it also needs sunlight, but water plays a vital role in the smooth functioning of a plant. Similarly, water plays a major role in the smooth running of our organs. As a person gets older less water is held in cells, and as people get older, they seem to lose their desire to drink plenty of water. So as you get older it would certainly be wise to keep up a high level of water drinking.

Our bodies do not have a water reserve to draw on. The way it works is on a priority distribution system: our bodies use the water that has already been taken in for the function of the organs that need the water and nutrients the most. When the organs do not get this water they cause us pain, disease and then eventual death.

The water drunk by a person should be processed by the kidneys and urinated if their kidneys are working properly. Because of the quantity of water that I now drink, I probably go to the toilet every couple of hours or so (not that you really wanted to know that but, I thought that I would tell you anyway, because this shows that my kidneys are processing the water!).

Rather than drinking water to relieve pain caused by dehydration many people will get painkillers either from their doctor or from the chemist. They don't realise the damage and the side-effects that painkillers can cause. In some people they can cause liver and kidney damage, also internal bleeding. Instead of painkillers just killing the pain, they can also kill the person, and only mask, the real problem of dehydration.

Indigestion

What I would do if ever I got indigestion, was take medication to stop the problem. On many occasions, I have ended up going to see my doctor, or having to visit the hospital because of the side-effects of the indigestion medication that I have taken. If you get ill or feel pain, the first thing to do, should always be to increase your water intake, before looking to medication in the form of tablets and medicine. Only turn to this form of treatment, if absolutely necessary. Stomach problems such as indigestion and ulcers are, in my opinion, major signs of dehydration. Much of the indigestion medication sold today in tablet or liquid form is actually damaging to our stomach. The side-effects from these pills are actually killing you. The most natural and safe protection to stomach problems is water.

Alzheimer's disease

Drinking large amounts of water even protects you right up into old age. Alzheimer's disease is usually caused by chronic dehydration of the brain cells. As the brain cells continually get dehydrated they begin to shrink and their functions are lost. Water is vital!

Colon

When waste materials are about to be removed from your body, they go through a part of the large intestine called the colon. Water is needed to soften the waste material so that your colon does not cause you to have pain or even tear so that waste matter escapes into your body and contaminates it. Eating fruit can also aid in the extraction of waste material from the body.

Arthritis

The word arthritis means inflammation of the joints; it is derived from two Greek words: athron meaning joints and itis, meaning inflammation. It is generally a chronic disease. There are different kinds of arthritis; the main ones are osteoarthritis and rheumatoid arthritis. Osteoarthritis is characterised by chronic degeneration of the joint cartilage and usually occurs in the older age group. Rheumatoid arthritis is a much more serious disease which affects most of the joints, muscles and tendons. For us to protect ourselves from arthritis, we need to increase our water intake. What an increased water intake does is hydrate the cartilage in our joints. Once the cartilage in our joints becomes dehydrated, major damage begins to happen. If this condition of dehydration is not addressed, bone can start to rub against bone in the joint area and cause extreme pain. If you are someone who has this condition, it would be wise to try to increase your water intake. There is a good chance that by increasing the amount of water you drink it may rehydrate your cartilage and relieve much of your pain. Massaging and bending the joint area will allow blood, as well as water into the joint. A friend of mine suffered terribly with arthritis, so I encouraged him to drink more water and to do light weights; his pain stopped.

Neck and back pain

Fluid is kept between the discs in the neck and back to cause lubrication for movement. This area of the body needs regular movement and a regular supply of water, so the discs remain lubricated.

Headaches

Headaches such as migraine are usually brought on by dehydration. Food can cause the body to become dehydrated so can excessive alcohol. Sometimes this condition can be brought about by the body overheating, due to not getting enough fresh air. The most sensible thing to do with regards to migraines is to prevent them rather than having to go through the pain of curing them. The best way to cure a migraine headache is to drink ice-cold water and get plenty of rest. To prevent this condition happening in the first place, one would need to avoid any food that may trigger this condition. Oranges, chocolate, alcohol, cheese and sugar or any other food that may cause this condition in you. Regular exercise and a healthy diet also help to prevent this condition.

Excess weight

When we get thirsty the sensation for thirst triggered in our body is similar to the sensation that we have when we get hungry. So a person might really be thirsty, but instead of drinking water which has no calories and will not cause weight gain, they eat excessively. Exercise is vital when it comes to not becoming overweight, because the larger a person's muscles are, the faster their metabolism becomes. Exercise needs to be done along with a healthy diet. We will look deeper into this subject later on in this book.

High blood pressure

High blood pressure is basically the result of extreme dehydration. The way our blood vessels are designed, is they adapt to the different stresses that are put upon them. So when there is less blood available, our blood vessels will shrink accordingly. When our overall bodily fluid is low, because of not drinking enough water, a similar thing will occur. When we allow our body to become dehydrated, 66% of the water contained inside our cells will be used; 26% of the water outside of the cell will be used and 8% from the blood. The closing of our vessels is what causes our blood pressure to go up. The remedy is to drink more water and to also do regular exercise. Regular exercise will increase our muscle size, in turn this will increase the size of our vessels to allow the flow of more blood. The fact that so much water is removed from the body's cells when there is a shortage of overall bodily fluid, it causes cell damage, when this state is continued over a period of time.

Swollen limbs

Due to dehydration, sometimes a person's body can begin to hold water so their limbs appear considerably swollen. Their doctor may prescribe diuretics which provide some relief from the condition at times, but do not cure the problem. The best way to get rid of water retention is to drink more water. When we begin to get dehydrated our body goes into starvation mode thinking that it isn't going to get water for a while. It then tries to hold on to as much water as possible. When you increase the quantity of water that you drink, your body begins to see that water is readily available, so it begins releasing excess water in the form of urine.

This tactic is used by bodybuilders, the day before they compete. They drink up to ten litres of water the day before they compete, and throughout the last week before the competition up to thirty litres! This tactic will cause them to release all excess water from their bodies in the form of urine, so as to show greater muscle definition.

High cholesterol

High blood cholesterol is basically your body telling you that it's dehydrated and needs water. Cholesterol is the human body's defence mechanism against dying of thirst. Cholesterol is a waxy fat in humans.

80% of the cholesterol contained in our body is manu-factured in our liver and is vital for our survival. The rest is taken into the body through meat, eggs, dairy products and prawns. What cholesterol does is form a paste to stop too much water being drawn out of the cells, to protect the cells from extreme dehydration. Cholesterol is like a tap that regulates the amount of water going in and out of your cells. When your body becomes low on water, it begins to produce more cholesterol, to stop more water from being drawn out of your cells. In turn this causes your blood to become highly concentrated with cholesterol which travels around your body, through your arteries and veins by protein packages called lipoproteins. While this cholesterol is travelling around your body obviously it will travel through places like your heart and lungs. After dehydration is continued, and cholesterol continues to build up, cholesterol deposits will block the main arteries in these areas. This may eventually cause a disease called atherosclerosis which is a hard-ening and inflammation of the artery wall which may eventually lead to death. Under normal circumstances excess cholesterol is metabolised by our liver. An increased intake of water will cause the body to stop producing cholesterol.

Asthma

About one in twelve adults are treated for asthma each year. It is a condition whereby the airways become irritated and inflamed. As a result of this mucus is produced and this makes it very difficult for air to flow into the lungs. In turn causes symptoms such as coughing, wheezing, tightness of the chest and breathlessness. Asthma and allergies are an indication that the body has a problem with dehydration. Because of this dehydration the body begins to increase its production of histamines.What will help and may well cure this problem is to slightly increase your salt intake and drink 4–6 pints of water a day (for adults). What you have to do also is be careful of the quantity of food and drink that you consume that contains potassium, as excess potassium can cause dehydration. Another good thing to do is regular exercise to strengthen your lungs. I have almost permanently stopped my asthma symptoms because of daily exercise, a very healthy diet, drinking large quantities of water and using my mental strength which is willpower to force myself to believe that I no longer have asthma. *Believe you me*, it works!

In this chapter we have discussed the fact that obesity is becoming an increasingly greater epidemic worldwide, as more countries become westernised and life becomes easier and people have less time. We also learnt that there are two kinds of health that are very important. For us to keep in good shape emotionally, we need to be careful of what we allow to enter into our minds. Another important thing that we learnt in this chapter is the need for us to live a peaceful orderly life. For us to do this we need to be self-disciplined: a disciplined mind is a healthy mind; an undisciplined mind is an unhealthy mind.

We then went on to see how absolutely vital water is for good health. Water is free but its value to our health is priceless! I am sure that you have heard the song or saying "The best things in life are free", and there is quite a bit of truth in this saying. I believe that many illnesses can be prevented and a lot have been cured by increasing water intake. We would need to also limit the amount of other drinks that we drink, such as coffee, tea and alcohol, and those containing high sugar such as fizzy drinks, since these all cause dehydration.

In the next chapter we are going to look at something else that's needed to have good physical health and that is to have a good diet and good nutrition.

6

HAVE *A GOOD*
DIET

To ensure good health: eat lightly, breathe deeply, live moderately, cultivate cheerfulness, and maintain an interest in life.
William Londen

I am sure that you have heard the saying "You are what you eat". Never could a truer set of words be said: what we eat has a tremendous effect on our health and wellbeing. Remember the survey on obesity mentioned in Chapter One.

Nutrition

13.5 million people suffer from heart disease and according to current statistics you have a 50% chance of developing heart disease. Heart disease is the cause of a quarter of all deaths of persons under 65 years of age. One human dies of heart disease every three minutes. Doctors will recommend medication for heart disease.

In the last chapter it mentioned the importance of drinking plenty of water to lower blood pressure in a person suffering from high blood pressure. According to the American Heart Association nearly one in three adults suffer from high blood pressure. One-third do not know it – high blood pressure is a silent killer. Some people have the disease for many years with no symptoms, so regular checks are vital.

Normal blood pressure – 120/80.

Pre-hypertension – 120–130 systolic pressure or diastolic pressure 80–89.

Stage 1 hypertension – 140–159 systolic pressure or diastolic pressure 90–99.

Stage 2 hypertension – Systolic pressure higher than 160 or diastolic pressure of 100 or higher.

The symptoms of high blood pressure are:

- Dizziness
- Headaches
- Nose bleeds

The causes are usually:

- Lack of water
- Smoking
- Stress
- Excess alcohol consumption
- Ageing

High blood pressure very often leads to heart disease. Blood pressure can be significantly lowered by taking in at least 1500mg of vitamin C per day. 600mg of vitamin E daily can reduce the risk of a heart attack in people that suffer from heart disease by 80 per cent according to nutrition experts at the University of California, Berkeley.

Many illnesses are caused by a person having a bad diet, and some cancers can be influenced by diet. Some medication given to patients with breast cancer can actually cause cancer of the ovaries, according to a study by the Emory University School of Cancer. By using nutritional alternatives you can avoid the terrible side-effects of many forms of medication.

Exercise can significantly reduce a person's chances of developing breast cancer and heart disease. Studies have shown that as little as $1^{1}/_{2}$–3 hours of brisk walking a week can reduce the chances of developing breast cancer or heart disease.

Researchers say also that eating five or more servings of fruit and vegetables, and choosing whole grains instead of processed foods, or red meat can greatly reduce a person's chances of developing heart disease or breast cancer.

Most people over the age of 55 suffer from arthritis to at least a small degree. One in every 100 people develops rheumatoid arthritis (RA). There are in fact 200 different kinds of arthritis; the most common one is osteoarthritis. What happens when a person develops osteoarthritis is the cartilage that protects the bone wears away, also the fluid contained between the bones dries up and bone can begin to rub against bone. This condition usually comes about through normal wear and tear of joints. A very sensible way to take the strain off your joints throughout your life, is to increase your muscle strength by physical exercise using weights. Younger people may get arthritis because of an accident or sports injury. Rheumatoid arthritis or inflammatory arthritis is a less common, but more severe form of arthritis. The immune system attacks and destroys the joint lining, making the joint painful, swollen and deformed. Persistent inflammation will eventually damage joints. Usually RA affects the small joints such as the fingers, thumbs, wrists, feet, ankles and knees but it can affect any joint in the body.

Symptoms are:

- Fever
- Feeling unwell
- Weight loss
- Muscle aches and pains

RA is worse for smokers. There is actually no proven test that can recognise the early signs of RA, because these signs could easily be mistaken for other illnesses. X-rays of a person's joints may begin to show signs of erosion. One cause of arthritis is more than likely a lack of exercise. To ease the pain doctors will recommend anti-inflammatory creams and tablets. In the USA Anti-inflammatory drugs are a $35 billion- dollar business: $20 billion for the drugs and a further $15 billion to fight the side-effects. Many thousands of people die from the side-effects of the medication. So once again the best and most cost-effective way to treat this condition is with natural alternatives, which will bring relief without the harmful side-effects.

Because the average person doesn't use natural alternatives to look after their health, humans live the last thirty years or more of their life, in poor health.

What you need to aim for in life, is high-level nutrition. This means that you are making available to your body the best possible nutrition, to keep your health at the highest standard, that you possibly can.

What is your highest level of nutrition?

It is your intake of nutrition that:

- Promotes your highest level of mental performance
- Promotes your highest level physical performance.
- Gives you the lowest instances of ill-health.
- Gives you the longest possible healthy lifespan.

There are basically fifty different nutrients that are essential for your health. By taking these nutrients your whole body, including your skeleton and joints, will become stronger and healthier.

High level nutrition will enable you to:

- Improve your mental health, alertness, mood and concentration.
- Increase your physical health.
- Extend your life span.
- Improve your resistance to infection and disease.

Some of the fifty essential nutrients

Fats
Linoleic acid; Linolenic acid.

Amino acids
Leucine; Lysine; Isoleucine; Threonine; Tryptophan; Methionine; Valine; Phenylalanine.

Minerals
Calcium; Magnesium; Phosphorus; Potassium; Sodium; Sulphur; Iron; Zinc; Copper; Manganese; Chromium; Selenium; Cobalt; Fluorine; Silicon; Iodine; Molybdenum; Vanadium; Arsenic; Nickel; Tin.

Vitamins
A (Retinol); B1 (Thiamine); B2 (Riboflavin); B3 (Niacin); B5 (Pantothenic acid); B6 (Pyridoxine); B12 (Cyanocobalamine); Folic acid; Biotin; C; K; D; E.
Additional

Carbohydrate; Fibre; Light; Oxygen; Water.

It isn't wise to go by RDA (recommended daily amount), because everyone has got a body unique to them. Our bodies are all different sizes and we all have different lifestyles. We are exposed to different quantities of substances that can damage our health (in other words different things that can drain our bodies of essential vitamins and minerals).

Analysis

It's good to continually analyse your health. When you see any signs in you of deteriorating health such as mouth ulcers, muscle cramps, lack of energy and easy bruising, take action to consume the correct nutrients you are lacking.

Another area that you would need to analyse is your lifestyle. If your lifestyle were to change whereby you begin to do more exercise, or begin experiencing a lot more stress in your life etc., you may have to change your general intake of nutrients. In the winter I take more vitamin C and echinacea capsules to boost my immune system.

Vitamin C

Most animals produce between 3,000 and 16,000mg of vitamin C within their bodies each day. Most vitamin C-producing animals are immune to most cancers and viral diseases. This illustrates how important it is for us to take in enough vitamin C each day. Unlike most mammals we humans do not have the ability to make our own vitamin C. The recommended daily amount of vitamin C is an ongoing debate. People who have diets that are high in vitamin C generally live longer, are a lot healthier and suffer from much less chronic illness. Vitamin C helps to keep blood vessels, tendons, ligaments, bones and the brain healthy. Vitamin C is also a highly effective anti-oxidant: it protects our cells from free radicals which can damage our cells, and cause cancer and heart disease.

Don't eat too much

Our bodies are not designed to be able to digest a lot of food in a single meal. The wisest course of action would be, to have light meals. I will have at times slightly larger meals. My next meal will definitely be small – this tricks my metabolism into speeding up thinking it will be getting another large meal, and I burn excess body fat. I try not to do this, but if you feel that your blood sugar is very low at times eat fruit between meals to keep your blood sugar and energy level up. This method doesn't agree with me, so as I said, I try to avoid eating between meals, but sometimes, I will have fruit between meals, if I feel that my blood sugar is very low.

Another good way to stop ourselves from eating too much, would be, to do some form of cardiovascular exercise; this will help you to control your appetite. Tests have shown that people with less active lifestyles, generally eat more, and find it harder to control their appetites. I have always said our bodies were designed to work hard.

Healthy lifestyle

- Don't eat late at night.
- Eat little and at set times 3–6 times a day.
- Eat mainly a fish and vegetable diet with half of your intake of food consisting of fruit, vegetables, seed sprouts, nuts and seeds. Eat mainly fish, but if you must have meat eat chicken breast with vegetables.
- Don't over-cook your food. If possible have your vegetables slightly under-done.
- Avoid food and drinks that contain sugar and, as I wrote in the last chapter, drink as much water as possible.
- Eat very little dairy products, refined wheat and grains.
- Exercise often and keep active.

Free radicals

Free radicals or oxidants are produced from burnt substances that enter into your body, such as: fried fat, burnt meat, exhaust fumes and cigarettes. Free radicals are potentially extremely dangerous to your body. What can be done to protect the body from this?

- Try to always eat whole foods.
- Eat a variety of different foods.
- Vitamin C and E are vital.
- Take a multivitamin.

Anti-nutrients

An anti-nutrient is food that we eat that takes more nutrients from our bodies to make use of it than it is giving to the body, for example junk food. Most cancers are related to the consumption of excess anti-nutrients. Things like painkillers, alcohol and the by-products of carbohydrates are also anti-nutrients.

The quantity of vitamin C that a smoker would need to take, to have the same blood level of vitamin C as a non-smoker is four times as much. The quantity of vitamin C that a heavy drinker would need to consume to have the same blood level of vitamin C as someone who doesn't drink is six times as much according to research done by some specialists.

Pesticides are also a hazard to our health. Tests have shown that three out of every four lettuces contain pesticides. Most fruit and vegetables contain pesticides and even if you wash them, tests have shown that 50–93% of the residue remains on the produce. The pesticide is actually designed to not be washed off by water. The only way round this is to buy organic produce where possible.

There are more than 3,000 man-made food chemicals and over 20,000 pesticides registered in the US. American agriculture is using 2.2 billion pounds of pesticide annually on more than 900,000 farms. The UK is reported as using 250,000 tons of food chemicals each year and 400 million litres of pesticide and herbicides sprayed on food crops. Billions of cigarettes and alcoholic drinks are consumed in the UK. We are also breathing in the industrial pollution of 50,000 chemicals.

From theses statistics can you see how vital it is, that we are careful about what we eat and the level of vitamins we are absorbing into our bodies.

The truth about our water

Calcium is in water because of its natural occurrence in the earth's crust. It comes from limestone, marble, calcite, dolomite, gypsum, fluorite and apatite. Calcium is needed for the skeleton, bone structure and teeth. 1.2kg of calcium is contained inside the human body; it is the most abundant mineral found in our bodies. It helps our bones and teeth alongside vitamin D. Many people don't realise that calcium helps our cells and muscles, and it also plays a major role in blood clotting. To stimulate these functions 1,000mg of calcium is needed daily for adults.

Natural mineral water, depending on its mineral make-up, can provide up to 600mg of calcium if you drink the recommended amount (2 litres), and that's only one- sixth of the RDA. Tap water only provides 60mg of calcium per 2 litres. When you filter water it not only removes the impurities but also most of the nutrients.

Fried food

Fried food produces in us dangerous chemicals known as free radicals. When we eat this kind of food it can damage cells, and increase the risk of cancer, heart disease and premature ageing. Fried food is an anti-nutrient: it destroys vitamin A and E which are essential for the protection of our good health.

If you choose to fry your food, it is much wiser to fry your food in olive oil or steam-fry with olive oil, whereby you would cover the frying pan with a lid and this would cause water to be created in the pan which will stop the oil from burning. Burning the oil or the food that you are frying may cause cancer.

The best way to cook your food is to either grill,

steam, boil or bake it. Try also not to over-cook the food because this also will destroy some or most of the nutrients in it.

Pharmaceuticals

You may be surprised to know that many medicines today are anti-nutrients. In the UK £577 million pounds is spent each year on painkillers such as aspirin and paracetamol.

Salicylic acid, the active ingredient in most painkillers, is a gastrointestinal irritant, increasing the permeability of the gut wall. This in turn upsets the absorption of nutrients, allowing incompletely digested foods to pass into the bloodstream and this weakens the immune system, causes inflammation, triggers intestinal bleeding and is an anti-nutrient. Four billion paracetamol tablets are taken worldwide each year. In the UK alone, 30,000 people end up in hospital each year, as a result of taking paracetamol. In 1994 in the UK 115 paracetamol-related deaths were reported. One in ten liver transplants is made necessary because of damage caused by an overdose of paracetamol. Twenty paracetamol can kill you; even one is extra work for the liver.

Antibiotics wipe out healthy gut bacteria that manufacture significant amounts of vitamin B. They also pave the way for unfriendly bacteria to multiply, which increases the risk of infection, stressing the immune system. The US National Institute of Health estimate that more than 50,000 tons of antibiotics are used every year throughout the world.

Eat a balanced diet

Most people today don't eat a balanced diet. We eat 2,300,000,000kg of sugar each year: that's 38kg per person. In the US sugar is 25% of total calorie intake. The UK government recommends 10 per cent sugar.

Ideal diet

- 65% Carbohydrate
- 15% Protein
- 20% Fat

Fats

There are basically two different kinds of fat: saturated and unsaturated fat. There are also two different kinds of unsaturated fats: monounsaturated fats, of which olive oil is a rich source, and polyunsaturated fats found in nuts, seed oils and fish.

Certain polyunsaturated fats contain omega 6 and omega 3 oils that are essential for the brain, nervous system, immune system, cardiovascular system and skin.

Protein

There are twenty-five different amino acids – different forms of proteins; these are the building blocks of the body.

The best quality protein foods in terms of amino acid balance are eggs, soya, meat, fish, beans and lentils. It is best to get your protein from vegetables or fish because meats tend to have hidden saturated fats. Many vegetables contain protein, for example seed foods like runner beans, peas, corn and broccoli, and these foods can help to neutralise excess acidity which can lead to loss of minerals, including calcium – which could cause a higher risk of osteoporosis among frequent meat-eaters.

The National Food Standards Agency recommends that 15% of your total calories should come from protein, or in other words you should have 40 grams of protein a day. The estimated daily requirement according to the UK Department of Health is 36 grams for women and 44 grams for men. Diets that contain very high levels of protein for losing weight are unwise and contain far too much protein most of the time.

Bodybuilders usually use as a rule of thumb 1 gram of protein to every 1 pound of pure muscle.

Essential amino acids

For a food source to contain complete protein it must contain the eight essential amino acids: tryptophan, valine, leucine, isoleucine, methionine, phenylalanine, threonine and lysine.

These eight essential amino acids can be found in meat, fish, eggs and soya.

Carbohydrate

Carbohydrate is the main fuel for the body and it comes in two forms: fast-release as in sugar, honey, malt, sweets and most refined foods, and slow-release, which is found in whole grain, vegetables and fresh fruit. The slow-release carbohydrates contain complex carbohydrate and/or more fibre, both of which slow down the release of sugar. Fast-release carbohydrates tend to give a burst of energy, then after a short period of time you feel drained, where as complex carbohydrates give a sustained level of energy, and therefore it would be wise to eat this form of carbohydrate.

Refined foods like sugar and white flour are anti-nutrients, and contain very low levels of the vitamins and minerals that are needed by the body. They are best avoided because they put a strain on the body. Regularly using fast-release carbohydrates can cause health problems and is best avoided. Some foods, like bananas, dates and raisins, contain faster release carbohydrates and are best kept to a minimum by people with glucose-related health problems.

Complex carbohydrates which are good to include in your diet: Bananas, Barley, Beans, Brown Rice, Chickpeas, Lentils, Nuts, Oats, Parsnips, Potatoes, Root Vegetables, Sweet Corn, Wholegrain Cereals, Wholemeal Breads, Wholemeal Cereals, Wholemeal Flour, Wholemeal Pasta, Yams.

Fibre

You should take in no less than 35 grams of fibre per day. It is quite easy to take in this amount of fibre. The fibre absorbs water into the digestive tract, making the food contents bulkier and easier to pass through the body. – Eat whole grains, fruits, nuts and lentils on a daily basis. Fruit and vegetable fibre help to slow down the absorption of sugar into the blood, helping to maintain good energy levels. Cereal fibre is particularly good at preventing constipation and putrefaction of food, which are underlying causes of digestive complaints.

Minerals

Like vitamins, minerals are essential for just about every body process. Calcium, magnesium and phosphorus help to make up the bones and teeth. Nerve signals vital for the brain and body depend on calcium, magnesium, sodium and potassium. Oxygen is carried in the blood by an iron compound. Chromium helps to control blood sugar levels. Zinc is essential for all body repair, renewal and development. Selenium and zinc help to boost the immune system. Brain function depends on adequate magnesium, manganese, zinc and other essential minerals. These are but a few of thousands of key roles that minerals play in human health.

We need large daily amounts of calcium and magnesium which are found in vegetables such as kale, cabbage and root vegetables. They are also abundant in nuts and seeds. Fruit and vegetables provide lots of potassium and small amounts of sodium, which is the right balance. All seed foods – which include seeds, nuts, lentils, dried beans, as well as peas, broad beans, runner beans and whole grains – are a good source of iron, zinc, manganese and chromium. Selenium is abundant in nuts, seafood, seaweed and seeds.

Too much meat could be bad for your health and bones

Meat-eaters have a low health rating. The risk of heart disease and cancer, particularly cancer of the stomach and colon, is directly related to meat consumption. So too are other diseases of the digestive system such as diverticulitis, colitis and appendicitis. Even more likely to result in cardiovascular disease is eating a lot of milk and dairy products. Overall a meat-eater is likely to visit the doctor or be admitted to hospital twice as often as a vegetarian and is more likely to suffer from degenerative disease ten years earlier than a vegetarian, according to a survey by Professor John Dickerson and Jill Davies from the University of Surrey.

Most people are in danger of eating too much protein rather than too little. Excess protein is a contributor to osteoporosis, over-acidity and many other common health problems.

Fish

While there is no doubt about the immense value of protein and essential fats in fish, fish is contaminated with man-made non-biodegradable toxins that tend to accumulate up the food chain (from plankton to small fish to bigger fish that eat the small fish and so on).

The same is true of animals that eat animals that ate pesticide-laden food.

Surveys have shown that all salmon have some contamination with PBCs and dioxins – industrial pollutants that don't biodegrade – and with dieldrins and toxaphene, which are pesticides / herbicides. Fish caught in the Pacific have much lower levels than fish caught in the Atlantic. Farmed salmon consistently have higher levels than wild salmon.

While I generally recommend eating more fish, it's easy to get confused by recommendations to avoid fish because of contamination with these and other toxic chemicals.

All fish contain mercury and generally the larger the fish the more the mercury.

Milk

Milk is not a very good source of many minerals. Manganese, chromium, selenium and magnesium are all found in higher levels in fruit and vegetables. Most important is magnesium, which works alongside calcium: you need twice as much magnesium to calcium. Seeds, nuts and crunchy vegetables like kale, cabbage, carrots and cauliflower give us both these minerals and others, more in line with our needs. Milk is after all designed for young calves, not adult humans.

Milk consumption is strongly linked with increased

risk of cardiovascular disease and also breast and prostate cancer. The higher a country's intake of milk, the higher its incidence of cardiovascular disease. Our bodies actually produce an antibody against milk, which certainly suggests it isn't an ideal food. On top of that 70% of people stop producing lactase, the enzyme to digest milk sugar, once they've been weaned.

Many children and adults suffer from milk allergy or intolerance. In many cases this is the result of lactose intolerance, resulting from this inability to digest lactose (milk sugar). The symptoms are bloating, abdominal pain, wind and diarrhoea, which subside on giving lactase. Probably equally common is an allergy to other dairy produce. The most common symptoms are blocked nose, excessive mucus production, respiratory complaints such as asthma and gastrointestinal problems. These are inflammatory reactions produced by the body when it doesn't like what you are eating. Such intolerances are likely to occur in people that consume dairy products regularly in large quantities. Instead of drinking milk, I take calcium tablets to get my calcium intake. Milk causes me to put on excess body fat and aggravates my asthma.

Fats

Fat is good for you! Eating the right kind of fat is absolutely vital for good health. Essential fats reduce the risk of cancer, heart disease, allergies, Alzheimer's disease, arthritis, eczema, depression, fatigue, infections, Pre-menstral tension (PMS) – the list of symptoms and diseases associated with deficiency is growing every year. When I first started dieting I used to be a fat-phobic, really I was depriving myself of essential health-giving nutrients and increasing my risk of poor health.

You need to be careful, however, of eating hard fat from dairy products, meat and most margarine.

The human brain is 60% fat and one-third of this should come from essential fats if you want to achieve your full potential for health and happiness. In fact, unless you go out of your way to eat the right fat-rich foods, such as seeds, nuts and fish, the chances are you are not getting enough good fat. Most people in the western world eat too much saturated fat, the kind that kills, and too little of the essential fats, the kind that heal.

Olive oil has mainly monounsaturated fat.

Sunflower seed has mainly polyunsaturated fat.

Polyunsaturated fats provide two essential fats: the linoleic acid family, known as omega 6, and the alpha-linolenic acid family known as omega 3. Fats should be 20% of your total caloric intake.

Omega 6

The grandmother of the omega 6 family is linoleic acid which is converted by the body into gamma-linolenic acid (GLA). Evening primrose oil and borage oil are the richest known sources of GLA. If you take these in supplement form you need less overall to obtain enough omega 6 fats. The ideal amount is around 100mg of GLA a day, equivalent to 1,000mg of evening primrose oil, or 500mg of high-potency borage oil – a capsule, a day.

GLA has two fats. Some GLA is converted into arachidonic acid. This type of fat is used to build the brain along with omega 3 fat DHA. GLA is also converted into DGLA (di-homo gamma linolenic acid) and from there into prostaglandins, which are extremely active hormone-like substances. The particular kind made from these omega 6 oils are called, series 1 prostaglandins. They keep the blood thin, which prevents clots and blockages, relaxes blood vessels, lowers blood pressure, helps to maintain the water balance in the body, decreases inflammation and pain, improves nerve and immune function and helps insulin to work, which is good for blood sugar balance. This is only the beginning, every year more and more health-promoting functions of prostaglandins are being discovered.

The best seeds for omega 6 are hemp, pumpkin, sunflower, safflower, sesame and maize. Walnuts, soya beans and wheatgerm are also rich in omega 6 fats.

Seeds are incredibly rich in essential fats, minerals, vitamin E and protein. You need a tablespoon a day for 100% health

Omega 3

The omega 3 fats EPA and DHA also make prostaglandins, which are essential for proper brain function, and affect vision, learning ability, coordination and mood. They reduce the stickiness of the blood, as well as controlling blood cholesterol and fat levels, improving immune function and metabolism, reducing inflammation and maintaining water balance. The best oils for omega 3 fats are flax (also known as linseed), hemp and pumpkin.

Foods that contain omega 3 are mackerel, herring, lake trout, swordfish, sardines, white fish, tuna and salmon or their oils. Mackerel contains the highest levels of omega 3.

People in Mediterranean countries, whose diets include large quantities of olive oil, have a lower risk of cardiovascular disease. However, this may be due to a number of positive factors about their diet, which includes a high intake of fruit, vegetables and relatively more fish than meat.

It is best to use monounsaturated oil, the best of which is olive oil. These don't generate harmful free radicals.

Coconut butter, is much better for you, than regular butter or lard (meat fat). This is because it's what's called a short-chain saturated fat. While health problems, such as increased risk of heart disease, have been associated with a high diet of animal fats, the same has not been shown for coconut butter or coconut milk.

Sugar

The human body is designed to run on carbohydrates. When you eat complex carbohydrates like whole grains, vegetables, beans or lentils or simple carbohydrates such as fruit, the body does exactly as it was designed to do. It digests these foods and gradually releases their potential energy. What is more, all the nutrients that the body needs for digestion and metabolism, are present in those whole foods. As humans we are naturally attracted to carbohydrates – sweetness.

Most concentrated forms of sugar, are devoid of vitamins and minerals, unlike the natural sources such as fruit. White sugar has about 90% of its vitamins and minerals removed. Without vitamins and minerals our metabolism becomes inefficient, contributing to poor energy and poor weight control.

Fruit contains simple sugar called fructose, which needs no digestion and can therefore enter the bloodstream quickly.

Some fruit, such as grapes and dates, also contain pure glucose and are therefore faster releasing. Apples on the other hand contain mainly fructose and are slow releasing. Bananas contain both and therefore raise blood sugar quite quickly.

Refined carbohydrates such as white bread, white rice and refined cereals have a similar effect to refined sugar, while oats are more complex and their release of sugar is slower. The process of refining or even cooking starts to break down complex carbohydrates into simple carbohydrates called malt (officially maltose), in effect predigesting them. When you eat simple carbohydrates you get a rapid increase in your blood sugar level and correspondingly a surge of energy. The surge however is followed by a drop as your body scrambles to balance your blood sugar level.

When your blood sugar level drops you feel hungry. The glucose in your bloodstream is available to your cells to make energy. When the levels are too high the body converts the excess to glycogen (a short-term fuel store mainly in the liver and muscle cells) or fat (our long-term energy reserve). When the levels are too low we experience a whole host of symptoms including fatigue, poor concentration, irritability, nervousness, depression, sweating, headaches and digestive problems. If you can control your blood sugar levels, the result is even weight and constant energy.

It isn't just about what you eat, it's also about the quantity that you eat, how you prepare it, what you eat with it – and what you drink with it.

Foods that contain refined sugar that we should try to avoid include: biscuits, cakes, pastries, chocolates, honey, jam, jellies, pizzas, ready-made foods and sauces, soft drinks, sweets and breakfast bars.

In this chapter we have looked at how important it is to have a balanced diet and how important it is to avoid anti-nutrients. In the next chapter we are going to look at how vital it is to make sure that we take in an adequate amount of vitamins daily.

7

VITAMINS
FOR *GOOD HEALTH*

He who enjoys good health is rich, though he knows it not.
Italian Proverb

Vitamin A

Vitamin A is known as retinol. Good sources of vitamin A are:

- Spinach
- Sweet potatoes
- Carrots
- Liver
- Eggs
- Cod liver oil
- Yams
- Cantaloupe
- Butternut squash
- Cheese
- Oily fish (mackerel)

Vitamin A deficiency is the most common nutritional deficiency in the world and is the leading cause of preventable blindness.

Vitamin A is needed to maintain:

- Healthy skin
- Good night vision
- Strong bones
- Strong teeth
- Strong immune system
- Proper red blood cell formation

A recommended daily amount of vitamin A is 0.7mg a day for men and 0.6mg a day for women.

Some researchers suggest that taking 1.5mg or more per day of vitamin A over many years may affect your bones and cause them to fracture easily.

Vitamin B1 (Thiamine)

You need 1mg of Thiamine per day.

Foods that contain Thiamine are:

- Pistachio Nuts
- Watermelon
- Hazelnuts
- Oatmeal
- Pasta
- Cashew nuts

- Green peas
- Fish
- Rice
- Sunflower seeds

Thiamin helps the body:

- Convert food into energy.
- Manufacture fat
- Metabolise protein
- Maintain normal function of the nervous system

Vitamin B2 (Riboflavin)

Riboflavin is a water-soluble B-complex vitamin. It helps every cell in your body produce energy and also protects the body from free radicals.

Foods that contain vitamin B2 are:

- Beef liver
- Mushrooms
- Milk
- Almonds
- Beef
- Broccoli
- Spinach
- Chicken
- Asparagus
- Salmon

RDA of vitamin B2 is 1.3mg per day for adults. If you take too much Riboflavin and you are healthy your body can eliminate the excess by means of your urine. Regularly taking large quantities of vitamin B2 tablets can give you eye problems.

Vitamin B3 (Niacin)

You need 6.6mg of Niacin for every 1,000 calories that you consume.

Foods that contain Niacin are:

- Peanuts
- Cereal
- Tuna
- Chicken
- Beef liver
- Turkey
- Lamb

Vitamin B6 (Pyridoxine)

Foods that contain vitamin B6 or Pyridoxine are:

- Salmon
- Nuts
- Brown rice
- Bananas

- Brussels sprouts
- Avocados
- Pork chops
- Potatoes
- Cantaloupe
- Halibut
- Tomatoes

Vitamin B12

Vitamin B12's primary functions are in the formation of red blood cells and in helping to maintain a healthy nervous system.

It can be found in:

- Eggs
- Meat
- Poultry
- Shellfish

Vitamin B15

Vitamin B15 is an antioxidant. It has got many beneficial effects and can reduce the symptoms of a hangover, prevent cirrhosis of the liver, stop pain caused by asthma and angina, reduce feelings of fatigue, lower your cholesterol level, extend the lifespan of your cells and prevent heart and gland disorder.

Vitamin B15 can be found in :

- Brown rice
- Pumpkin
- Sesame seeds
- Wheat
- Brewing yeast

Note: Cooking at high temperatures (over 84°C) can destroy B vitamins.

Vitamin C

Vitamin C helps the bones, ligaments, tendons and blood vessels. It can reduce the severity of colds, acting as a natural antihistamine. Slightly increasing your daily amount of vitamin C can often lessen the duration of a cold should you get one. Vitamin C taken orally also helps wounds heal faster. It is a major help in having a strong immune system to protect the body against free radicals (a highly reactive byproduct of metabolism that can damage tissue) and could be classed as one of the first lines of defence against heart disease and most cancers. (Not that it cures these illnesses, but it strengthens the immune system.) Take between 1000 and 2000mg per day.

Foods that contain Vitamin C are:

- Sweet red peppers
- Strawberries
- Oranges
- Brussels sprouts
- Greens
- Grapefruit
- Cantaloupe
- Cabbage
- Tomatoes
- Blackberries
- Bananas
- Peaches
- Watermelon
- Kiwi (extremely high level)
- Mangoes
- Grapes
- Lemons

Vitamin D

Vitamin D helps to:

- Maintain strong teeth and bones
- Support the immune system
- Regulate blood sugar levels
- Prevent diabetes
- Prevent high blood pressure

Foods that we can get vitamin D from are:

- Salmon
- Cod liver
- Sardines
- Eggs

It is wise not to take too much vitamin D into your body because it can cause serious health problems such as kidney stones, heart disease and bone loss.

Vitamin E

Vitamin E protects the cell membranes as well as keeping our skin, heart, circulation, nerves, muscles and red blood cells healthy. Antioxidants such as vitamin E protect your cells from free radicals, which can cause cell and tissue damage that may in some cases lead to cancer or cardiovascular disease.

Vitamin E can be found in:

- Fruit
- Nuts
- Vegetables
- Corn
- Corn oil
- Apples
- Bananas
- Blackberries

Calcium

Foods that you can get calcium from are:

- Milk
- Cheese
- Broccoli
- Yogurt
- Okra
- Nuts
- Bread
- Sardines
- Pilchards

Calcium helps to:

- Regulate muscle contraction
- Build strong bones and teeth
- Make blood clot normally
- Lower blood pressure
- Protect against colon cancer
- Protect against breast cancer

It is wise to consume 1500mg of calcium or less each day. Taking too much calcium could cause stomach pain and diarrhoea.

Potassium

Potassium is a mineral that is found in most foods, including:

- Bananas
- Vegetables
- Pulses
- Nuts
- Seeds
- Milk
- Fish
- Shellfish
- Beef
- Chicken
- Turkey
- Bread

Potassium balances body fluids but taking too much potassium can cause stomach pain, diarrhoea and nausea. Your natural diet should really give you all of the potassium that you need: for adults that is 3500mg.

Iron

The foods that contain iron are:

- Liver
- Beans
- Nuts
- Meats

- Apricots
- Watercress
- Curly kale

Men should consume 8.7mg and women 14.8mg of iron each day. It is quite easy to get this quantity of iron from your daily diet.

Iron helps to make red blood cells to carry oxygen around your body.

If you consume too much iron it can cause constipation, nausea, vomiting, stomach pain or even death.

Magnesium

Foods that contain magnesium are:

- Spinach
- Nuts
- Bread
- Fish
- Meat
- Dairy products

Magnesium helps the parathyroid gland to function correctly and helps to transform the food we eat into energy.

You should get enough magnesium from your natural daily diet. Taking too much magnesium can cause diarrhoea. Try to have only 400mg of magnesium or slightly less each day.

8

HEALTHY RECIPES

New Tuna Niçoise

Ingredients

500g potatoes, halved
200g fine green beans
6 quail's eggs, boiled – cool in cold water
1 romaine lettuce, shredded (heart only)
1 small can tuna, in spring water, drained

For the dressing:
1 tbs capers, roughly chopped
1 red chilli, seeded and finely chopped
1 small garlic clove, crushed
1 tsp olive oil
1 lime, grated rind and juice
1 pinch fine sea salt and freshly ground black pepper

Method

Cook the potatoes in a large pan of boiling salted water for 15 minutes, adding the beans to the pan for the last 2–3 minutes of cooking time.

To make the dressing, stir together the capers, chilli, garlic, olive oil and lime rind and juice, adding salt and pepper to taste.

Drain the potatoes and beans then cool under running water until completely cold. Shell and halve the eggs.

Loosely toss together the lettuce, tuna, potatoes, beans, eggs and dressing. Serve the salad as soon as it is tossed.

Low Fat Simple Chicken Curry

Ingredients

½ tbs turmeric
1 tbs curry powder
½ tbs coriander powder
1 tbs olive oil – extra virgin
½ tbs chopped onions
1 garlic clove
½ chilli pepper
Mixed herbs – dried or freshly chopped
1 chicken breast cut into 6–7 pieces
½ pint chicken stock- cube or fresh
Gravy mix? – Only if you want thicker sauce

Method

Coat the breast of chicken with all of the ingredients except the olive oil and stock. Then marinate in the fridge overnight, so that the flavour of all of those ingredients go to the centre of each of the pieces of chicken.

Slowly cook the chicken in the olive oil in a covered saucepan for 10 mins, the bigger the quantity the longer the cooking time. It should create its own stock when nearly cooked, but add extra stock as needed. Thicken if you would like a thicker sauce.

Serve with brown rice, chopped tomato, chopped coriander and chopped spring onion.

Quick Vegetable Curry

Ingredients

Diced yam
Diced plantain
Diced carrot
Diced onion
Diced potato
Pinch mixed herbs
Vegetable stock or cube
Aubergine
1 clove garlic
1 tbs olive oil
Courgette
½ tbs turmeric
½ tbs curry powder
½ tbs coriander powder
1 small chilli pepper
2 cardamom seeds
Pinch salt

Method

Cut all of the vegetables into ¼-inch dice. Have equal quantities of all of the vegetables in accord with the amount of people that you are cooking for. Cook everything, except the vegetable stock in a covered saucepan slowly for 10–15 mins. Add vegetable stock and simmer for 8 mins.

Serve with brown rice, chopped tomato, chopped coriander and chopped spring onion.

Baked Salmon and Lentil Hotpot

Ingredients

Sliced white or sweet potatoes
Sliced onions
Mixed herbs
Lentils
Chilli peppers
Salmon supreme
1 ltr fish or chicken stock
2 tbs olive oil
Mixed spices e.g. coriander powder, curry powder.
Chopped garlic

Method

Coat the salmon supreme in the spice mixture and leave to marinate.

Soak the lentils for at least 4–6 hrs, and then boil in the fish or chicken stock until slightly soft. Slowly cook the garlic, onions and chilli peppers in the olive oil along with the mixed herbs. Add the cooked lentils once the onions are slightly soft. Cook for 5 mins, then place the mixture into a casserole or baking dish. Layer the potatoes onto the top of the mixture. Brush the tops of the potatoes with some of the olive oil. Then bake the mixture at 200°C (gas mark 6) for approx 30 mins until the potatoes are brown on top.

Brush the top of the salmon with olive oil then place on a flat baking tray, greased with olive oil and bake for approx 10 mins until cooked.

The same recipe can be used for breast of chicken or any fish of your choice.

Stir-Fry Chicken Noodles

Ingredients

1 onion
1 carrot
1 leek
Herbs
Mange touts
Bean sprouts
Olive oil
Diced or strips of chicken breast
Chilli peppers
1 tbs cashew nuts
Coconut (desiccated)
Garlic (chopped)
Noodles (brown if possible, boiled in water till cooked)
1 tbs oyster sauce
1 tbs soya sauce
Spices

Method

Marinate the chicken in spices and some of the garlic for at least 6–8hrs in a container in the fridge. Cut all of the vegetables into thin strips (or buy a ready-made packet of stir-fry mix already cut from the supermarket). Fry the chicken in the olive oil. Add the vegetables and cook for 2 mins. Add noodles and the rest of the ingredients and stir. Cook for 3 mins then it should be ready.

This recipe can also be done by replacing the chicken with any fish of your choice, or for a healthy vegetarian choice you could replace the chicken with kidney beans or a variety of beans or even tofu.

Oat Cake

Ingredients

½kg oats
1 banana
3 tbs raisins
6 tbs honey
5 tbs nuts of your choice (almonds, cashews)
2 tbs olive oil

Method

Crush the nuts either in a food processor or in a cloth, rolling over it with a rolling pin. Crush the banana with a fork. Mix all of the ingredients together. Grease a baking tray with olive oil and cover with greaseproof paper. Spread the mix evenly across the paper. Then bake at 180°C (gas mark 4) until brown and cooked.

Chicken or Fish Stock

Ingredients

Onions
Leeks
Peppercorns
Celery
Chicken or fish bones
Herbs

Method

For brown chicken stock use roasted bones and vegetables (you could also shallow fry the vegetables and bones in olive oil).

Put all of the ingredients into a saucepan and cook slowly for 10 mins. Cover the chicken or fish with water, and then bring to the boil and skim the scum off the surface of the water. Then allow it to simmer – for fish 20 mins and for chicken 4–6 hrs – and keep topping up with water as needed. Once ready strain off the bones and store in the fridge or freezer once cool. For a stronger flavour put the stock back into a saucepan and boil on the stove until the liquid reduces by two-thirds and then put into containers and use when needed.

Fruit Salad

Ingredients

Pineapple
Apple
Orange segments
Banana
Strawberries
Mango
Kiwi
Lemon juice
Orange juice

Method

$1/4$-inch dice all of the ingredients and mix together. Then half fill the container that the fruits were mixed in with orange juice and a dash of lemon juice.

Chicken or Fish Salad

Ingredients

Diced chicken or fish, seasoned (cooked)
Lettuce of choice, shredded
Cherry tomatoes cut in $1/2$
Cucumber, sliced or diced
Chopped spring onions

Method

Toss all of the ingredients together.

Low Fat Dressing

Ingredients

> 6tbs mustard of choice (English, French or grain)
> ½ pt vinegar (white wine or balsamic)
> 1 pt olive oil
> Freshly chopped basil

Method

Mix the mustard with the vinegar. Then slowly drizzle the olive into the mix and add chopped basil.

How to lose weight very quickly

To lose weight quickly, you need to keep your calories as low as possible. Remember also, what has been stated throughout this book: no discomfort, no progress (or if you like no pain, no gain).

When you cut your calories it is normal to feel a bit tired or weak. Sometimes you may feel a bit depressed, but keep going!

Try to keep your carbohydrate intake as low as possible while you are dieting, but don't cut carbohydrates out completely because that is bad for your health. As has been discussed earlier in this book always drink plenty of water.

Diet to lose weight

Breakfast: Oats with sliced banana (very small amount)

Lunch: Chicken salad

Dinner: Fish salad

Try to eat all of this before 7pm. Try also to eat as little oats and banana as possible and gradually eat less each day. The salad consists of only lettuce, cucumber and tomato with no dressing.

Once the weight is lost try not to eat a lot and eat a variety of healthy foods.

For my own personal diet I have:

Breakfast: 2 chicken breasts, porridge

Lunch: Tuna salad with brown rice, boiled potato, corn on the cob, butter beans, cashew nuts and vegetables

Dinner: Salmon or other fish, salad and vegetables

Once a week I will eat other foods or in some ways you could call it a bad diet day, but not too bad, so that my body will always be healthy and look good!

Vitamins that I take

Multi-vitamins
Calcium – helps bones
Echinacea – helps immune system
Vitamin C with zinc – helps immune system
Glucosamine – helps protect joints
Omega 3, 6 and 9 with flax seed oil
Garlic capsules – help immune system
Amino acids – help muscle growth
Cod liver oil – protects joints

In this chapter we have looked at healthy recipes. Along with a healthy diet, exercise is needed. This is what we will be looking at in the next chapter.

9

EXERCISE –
FOR *GOOD HEALTH*

*The sovereign invigorator of the body is exercise and of all the
exercises walking is best.*

Thomas Jefferson

Brisk walking is completely free of charge; it's also a
great means of transport to get you from one place to
another. Walking can help you to reduce your weight.
A 60kg (or nine and half stone) person walking at
3mph burns 99 calories per half hour. Brisk walking at
4mph burns 150 calories. The heavier you are, the
more calories you will burn. Walking causes the body
to realease serotonin so you will fell happier and
calmer throughout the day. You will have greater
vitality, more get up and go, although for the first
week or so you might feel a little more tired than
usual. Another benefit is that you will sleep better.
The list goes on: it can help to prevent high blood
pressure, heart disease, stroke, different forms of
cancer and it even strengthens your bones.

So why not start off briskly walking for ten minutes
each day – you can get off the bus one stop early and

walk the rest of the way to work, and then gradually build up the distance and speed.

It would be a good idea to join a gym. The better the standard of the members going to the gym, the better *you* will be, just as if someone played golf with Tiger Woods, they would eventually be a much better golf player than if they spent a lot of time playing with someone who had just started to learn golf. Most leisure centres and gymnasiums make you do an induction before they will allow you to have member-ship, to cover themselves for legal reasons. When they show you around the gymnasium and you get the chance to try out the different machines and also the free weights, choose to put in your training routine the machines and free weights that you get the best results from. Once again they will be the machines and free weights that cause your muscles the most pain and discomfort. It would also be beneficial if you can get a training partner, preferably someone more experienced than you, who can push you. I personally do not use a training partner because most people can't handle the level of pain that I put my body through.

Home Training with no equipment
Even if you have very little money, equipment or time you can still keep fit and in good shape at home.

Press-ups

Press-ups work the chest, the back of the arms (*triceps*) and also the core muscles (*stomach, spine and hip muscles*). The primary muscle used is the chest (*pectoral muscle*).

To perform the exercise lie flat on your stomach.

Then place the palms of your hands flat on the floor and push your body up off the floor until your arms are straight.

You should also be on the tips of your toes.

Control your body back down again close to the floor by bending your arms and repeat this exercise for as many repetitions as you can.

Each time you perform this exercise constantly have the goal to do more and more repetitions.

Sit-ups

The sit-up is a strength-training exercise commonly performed with the aim of strengthening the abdominal muscles and hip flexors. This begins with lying with the back on the floor, typically with the knees bent in an attempt to reduce stress on the back muscles and spine, and then elevating both the upper and lower spine from the floor until everything superior to the buttocks is not touching the ground. Repeat the movement for ten repetitions and then constantly increase the repetitions each time you do the exercise. Some now consider it dangerous and relatively ineffective, and it has been replaced with the crunch in many training programmes as an abdominal exercise.

Back raises

To do back raises you need to keep your back and legs straight, bend forward and try to touch your toes and then stand upright again. By repeatedly doing the motion you are doing back raises. This exercise is to be performed while in a standing position.

By performing this exercise you would be strengthening your lower back and your hamstrings.

Squats

The squat is a lower body exercise used in strength training and an essential movement in the sport of weightlifting. This exercise's main emphasis is on the quadriceps and the glutes but it also involves the hamstrings, the calves and the lower back. The squat is often called "the king of exercises" by those who believe it capable of inducing more and faster muscle growth than any other exercise.

The squat is performed by bending the legs at the knees and hips, lowering the torso between the legs, and then reversing direction to stand up straight again. The torso leans forward to maintain balance. It acts as a supporting structure, unlike its role in the dead lift. Proper technique is critical, otherwise very serious injuries or gradual injury over a period of time can occur. The back must maintain its natural curvature and not "round out" (excessive lumbar or thoracic kyphosis), otherwise excess strain can be placed on the spine and cause serious injury. Lifting belts can be used to help support the lower back.

Squats can be performed with or without weights.

It would be wise to get a set of weights!

Home exercise routine

Press-ups 10 reps
Sit-ups 10 reps
Squats 10 reps
Back raises 10 reps

In your home exercise routine start off doing as many reps as you can in each of the different exercises. Then add an extra 5 repetitions each time you train at home. If you cannot increase by 5 repetitions try to increase by 2 repetitions.

One other point. I am going to remind you, it's going to be painful. I am sure that you are used to that fact by now, because that's what progress is all about. No discomfort, no progress.

It's a good practice to do this training routine 3–5 times a week.

Throughout this book the truth that has constantly been stated is: no discomfort, no progress. The only way to have a good-looking healthy body is to use your willpower to diet and exercise to the full. No one gets it handed to them on a plate.

Regularly read and re-read this book to keep motivated!

What are you waiting for – start getting your health in order now!

It is up to you how you organise what days you will train your different body parts. It might be wise to try out different combinations of body part training and see which one works best for you.

I try to keep my repetitions as high as possible in my weight training routine sometimes doing as many as 50-60 repetitions! With heavier weights I will do 6-8 reps, so that I am combining cardiovascular training with strength training.

You might choose to add cycling, swimming, brisk walking, skipping, dancing or any other form of cardiovascular exercise to your training routine, so as to exercise your heart and lungs and give definition to your body by burning body fat.

I try to do almost every exercise there is for each body part. This gives shape to my muscles. I work the muscle until I can't do any more, then I know that muscle has been trained to the full!

My gym exercise routine

Monday
Rest

Tuesday
Back and triceps

Wednesday
Rest

Thursday
Shoulders and biceps

Friday
Legs

Saturday
Rest

Sunday
Chest and forearm